John Constantine
HELLBLAZER

fearandloathing

GARTH ENNIS
writer

STEVE DILLON
artist

TOM ZIUKO
colors

GASPAR
TODD KLEIN
letters

GLENN FABRY
original covers

WARREN ELLIS
introduction

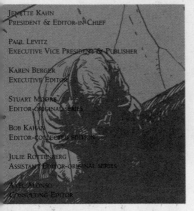
JOHN CONSTANTINE, HELLBLAZER: FEAR AND
LOATHING
ISBN 1 85286 819 8

This is a book about lives being ground into shit.

It's funny stuff.

I imagine a lot of you holding this book in your hands, or between your stumps or whatever, are familiar with the names Ennis and Dillon from PREACHER, which, in addition to being the best regular comic published today, is also bloody funny. This book has its funny bits, too; the piss jokes and liberal sprinklings of rabbit shit are the bad seeds of PREACHER's screaming laugh track.

The rest of you, I guess, might have flicked through this volume and are having problems with the fact that I am characterizing such things as The Death of Hope, Horrible Beatings, Disgusting Murder, Sexual Treachery, The Killing of Love and Stark Religious Horror

as funny. Tough. Garth and Steve are comfortable with these themes. It may be gallows humor, but they're at least stopping to draw a cock on the wood before they swing.

Garth Ennis is the Irishman who started writing comics in order to escape from university, characterizing the students he was locked up with as "a pack of wankers." As I write this, the bastard's just starting a month-long trip across the States with his mate Jeff, while I sit here locked in my Essex castle writing the intro for his book. It's a rough old life, being in comics. Steve Dillon has been drawing comics professionally since he was about four years old. He has about eighty-five kids and lives in Luton, because somebody has to.

"WE NEVER LIKED YOU ANYWAY."

introduction by **Warren Ellis**

This book comprises the opening shots of their collaboration. Garth had already been writing HELLBLAZER for a couple of years, taking great joy in making previous regular artist Will Simpson draw disgusting things. Will, an excellent artist, responded gamely and professionally, as he always does, but his heart was never in the horror. Will is a very nice man, and so his waking hours are not consumed with daydreams of gratuitous claret and eviscerated royalty. It was fine work, but what Steve brought to the book, in addition to his phenomenal storytelling skills (and I don't think there's a better storyteller than Steve Dillon in the monthly comic-book business right now), was an utter relish for the punished meat and torn skin. I guess that when you've worked for British publishers for as long as Steve had, you develop a higher and finer touch for these things. Garth responded in the only way he could, being Garth: he turned up the volume.

But before I get too far into that, it's worth spending a few moments with the other important character in the book: John Constantine. Frequently painted as a mystic investigator in some kind of bastardized Chandlerian tradition, Society's Knight riding against the Bad Craziness in the dark, John is one of horror fiction's more complex characters. Rather than Philip Marlowe with a magic kit, John is instead Society's Bastard, locked inside the world he hates, angry and twisted, holding a small, poisoned set of ethics to his chest. And that last point is possibly the only thing that really makes him different from the rest of them. That's what makes him wake with anger and lie down with it. That little voice that says Fucking People Over Is Wrong, and No One Else Should Have To Live Like This.

In the (Christ! It's damn near a) decade since his creation, John Constantine has gone from the young English occult wideboy of Alan Moore's initial vision to the troubled and aging adrenaline addict of Jamie Delano's bleakly poetic writing, who grew crushed by the appalling weight of his own terrible life during

Jamie's often brilliant forty episodes. The strength of the character, that has him remain so clearly the same man even when viewed through two or three different writers' eyes, is that he is a terrific mouthpiece for anger.

Jamie's final episode of his run on the book saw John finding some kind of personal closure, having finally turned his anger inward. Once Garth got moving — and FEAR AND LOATHING really does signal Garth hitting top speed on HELLBLAZER — John Constantine, forty and fucked off, got angry with *everything*.

It works because John is very clearly given things worth protecting from the world. In this piece, his anchor and his grail is his girlfriend Kit. A complex piece of work in herself, and John's superior in pretty much everything, she's another facet of the strong, intelligent woman that Garth's been writing (probably unconsciously) from his earliest work, *Troubled Souls*, to PREACHER. The world in which he wants to live with her is symbolized by the clasp of friendship, another major theme of Garth's run on HELLBLAZER and best displayed in the "party issue" contained in this book.

What's John protecting these things from? Authority. With the capital A. These are stories about what authority does to people, about the poison in its foundations. You can substitute Authority for Government, for the Establishment, even for God, and it all means the same thing: someone exerting control they did not earn and do not deserve, grinding lives into shit largely because they feel like it. This is where Garth and Steve found the anger, in people using our fear on us, locking us in the black iron prison of mediocrity and ignorance.

What follows is among the very best horror work of the 1990's. It retains the occult connections, but what sets it apart from the sad, played-out "dark fantasies" that you'll find on the shelf next to it is its clear knowledge that real horror is perpetrated not by eye-rolling pantomime monsters, or pale things in black with stupid names. Real horror comes only from people. Just people. They're the scariest things in the world.

Hold on, let me light up here...okay, where's the checklist? I've pretty much covered the "I know Garth, which is why I'm writing this" bit, done the quick bio bit, done the history bit and the sad litcrit bit, praised Garth and Steve to the skies so's I can get drinks out of 'em...right, I'm finished. Now go and read the sodding book.

Warren Ellis
Southend
August 1996

(*Warren Ellis writes comics and tells lies for a living. His works include the wholesale butchery of the Marvel Universe in* Ruins, *the politicizing and fetishizing of super-heroes in* Stormwatch *and* DV8, *and the liberal flinging-around of human meat in* Druid. *Currently preparing the political sf series* TRANSMETROPOLITAN *for Helix, Warren Ellis lives in England with his partner and daughter, and smokes a lot.*)

est horror work of the 1990's."

THERE'S AN OLD GRAVEYARD SOUTH OF LIVERPOOL, WHERE THE IRISH SEA SPEWS TOXIC SHIT ACROSS A LONELY SHORE...

NO ONE COMES HERE NOW, NOT EVEN TO BE BURIED. NOTHING WAKES THE SLEEPERS, NOTHING TRAMPS ACROSS THEIR BEDS...

EXCEPT FOR NOSY BASTARDS LIKE ME, OF COURSE.

PRETTY SOON NOW I'LL FINISH THIS FAG, AND I'LL PICK UP THE SPADE...

AND THEN I'LL START DIGGING.

END OF THE LINE

GARTH ENNIS • writer   **STEVE DILLON** • artist
TOM ZIUKO • colors   *gaspar* • letters   **STUART MOORE** • editor

OH, JESUS...

HERE, HOLD ON-- YOU THINK *I* GAVE HER THIS?

WHO ELSE?

BLOODY HELL, CHERYL! I'VE MESSED ME LIFE UP GOOD AND PROPER WITH THIS BOLLOCKS -- WHY WOULD I WANT TO DO THE SAME TO *GEMMA*?

SHE'S ME *NIECE*...

SHE'S MY DAUGHTER.

AW, CHERYL... I SWEAR TO GOD I DIDN'T GIVE HER THIS, OKAY? I MEAN, DID *SHE* SAY I DID?

NO. SHE WON'T TELL ME ANYTHING ABOUT IT.

D'YOU WANT ME TO HELP HER?

...AND WHEN HE CAME BACK AFTER HE SAID WE WOULDN'T SEE HIM AGAIN, I MEAN, I THOUGHT HE WAS STARTING TO SORT HIMSELF OUT...

BUT I FOUND GEMMA WITH THAT...THING, AND HE WAS THE FIRST ONE I THOUGHT OF, Y'KNOW?

AW, I DO OF COURSE, CHERYL...

BUT YOUR WEE BROTHER, YOU KNOW WHAT HE'S LIKE-- YOU AND GEMMA ARE A REAL COMFORT TO HIM. HE WOULDN'T HURT YOU IN A MILLION YEARS, LOVE.

OH, BUT YOU TOO, KIT--YOU'VE BEEN BRILLIANT FOR HIM!

ER...

SO, DOES TONY KNOW ABOUT ALL THIS?

OH GOD, NO. IT'D DESTROY HIM, THE STATE HE'S IN...

SANDRA'S BEEN REALLY HORRIBLE TO ME, UNCLE JOHN. SHE NICKED BARRY OFF ME AT TINA'S PARTY AN' ALL-- AN' SHE'S MEANT TO BE ME *FRIEND!*

HE SAID HE'D PUT A CURSE ON ME.

I...I CAN'T SAY--!

AW, GEM...

SHE'S THE ONE THE PINS ARE IN ON THE PHOTO, YEAH?

GEM, WHERE'D YOU GET THIS?

A CURSE--? WHO SAID IT, LUV? WHAT'S HIS NAME?

BECAUSE RIGHT THEN, I WANTED TO KNOW WHAT TO PUT ON THE FRIGGER'S GRAVE.

DAD'S GHOST, AND THE MAN--I MEAN, HADN'T THE KID BEEN THROUGH ENOUGH?

OH GOD....

ROB- ROBBIE BROOKS.

R.I.P.

HE'S TINA'S BROTHER. I THOUGHT HE WAS JUST A DICKHEAD, LIKE. BUT HE CAME UP TO ME WHEN I WAS ANGRY AT THE PARTY...

"HE TOLD ME HE COULD HELP ME GET BACK AT SANDRA. SHOWED ME ALL THESE BOOKS AN' EVERYTHING--IT LOOKED LIKE DEVIL WORSHIP STUFF. WITH ALL THESE STARS AN' LATIN WRITING, Y'KNOW?

"SOMEONE TOOK THE PHOT AT THE PARTY ROBBIE SAID WAS GOOD FO THE MAGIC.

"I WAS JUS ABOUT TO PRICK ME THUMB AN PUT BLOOD ON IT..."

"AN' HE GAVE ME THE BOARD AN' MADE ME SWEAR NOT TO TELL.

AN' THEN ME MAM WALKED IN. SHE NEAR HAD A FIT.

THANK CHRIST.

'M SORRY.

S'OKAY, LUV. S'OKAY. I'LL FIX EVERY- THING UP, RIGHT?

GEM... YOU'RE A SMART KID, LUV. WHY'D YOU WANT TO MESS ABOUT WITH THIS CRAP?

WELL... I DUNNO... I THOUGHT I COULD GET SANDRA. I KNOW IT WAS SORT OF WICKED, LIKE...

BUT IT WAS ALSO SORT OF EXCITING, TOO.

WELL? HOW'S MY LITTLE MONSTER, THEN?

YOU'RE NOT MAD AT ME?

NO.

WELL?

SOME BASTARD'S TRYING TO GET HER INTO MAGIC.

JESUS, IT'S JUST LIKE *I* STARTED OUT--THEY MAKE YOU THINK IT'S THE GREATEST THING SINCE SLICED BREAD--!

I'LL HAVE TO SORT THIS WANKER OUT.

AND THEN I'LL HAVE TO PUT THE FEAR OF GOD INTO GEMMA, SO SHE STOPS IT *HERE*...AW, SHIT.

WHY DON'T...WHY DON'T YOU LET *ME* TALK TO GEMMA?

ON THE OTHER SIDE OF LIVERPOOL, AND HALF A PACKET OF SILK CUT LATER, I FOUND THE SQUAT WHERE BROOKS WAS SUPPOSED TO LIVE.

ANGER MAKES THINGS SEEM EASY. GO OUT, FIX THE BASTARD, FEEL BETTER. GO HOME.

IF ONLY.

I'M LOOKING FOR A LAD CALLED BROOKS.

SO WHAT?

O1!

PISS OFF, BOLLOCKS.

I'M NOT AFRAID OF *YOU*, PAL! I DO **KARATE**!

YOU'RE BROOKS. YOU'RE THE ONE GIVES CURSE BOARDS TO KIDS, EH?

WHAT? HAVE YOU BEEN TALKIN' TO THAT *MASTERS* BITCH?

SHE'S *MY NIECE*, YOU FAT PILE OF SHIT. *WATCH IT!*

YOUR--? JESUS! JOHN CONSTANTINE! IN MY HOUSE!

OH *BLOODY HELL*--!

OH KIT, IT'S *BRILLIANT!* ARE YOU *SURE,* LIKE?

AYE, YOUR UNCLE JOHN WANTED YOU TO HAVE SOMETHING NICE FOR CHRISTMAS...

I'M TELLIN' YOU, GEMMA, YOU'RE GONNA KNOCK 'EM *DEAD* IN THAT.

THANKS. YOU'RE DEAD GOOD TOGETHER, YOU TWO. I MEAN, JOHN NEVER REALLY LASTED WITH ANYONE BEFORE, Y'KNOW?

MM. DID YOU MEET MANY OF HIS OTHER GIRLFRIENDS?

WELL...EMMA WAS UP WITH HIM A FEW TIMES, BUT I WAS ONLY LITTLE THEN. SHE WAS NICE.

SHE WAS AYE.

SHAPES
FASHION

SALE!

SALE 20%

BUT ME MAM, RIGHT-- SHE THINKS YOU'RE GREAT, SHE DOES. SHE SAYS YOU'RE UNCLE JOHN'S *LAST CHANCE.*

DOES SHE, NOW?

SOMETIMES PEOPLE ARE JUST THEMSELVES, NOT WHAT OTHER PEOPLE HOPE THEY'LL BE.

HERE, D'YOU FANCY A PIZZA?

YEAH!

THAT'S WHY HE WAS WORRIED ABOUT YOU, LOVE. HE DOESN'T WANT YOU MUCKING UP YOUR LIFE THE WAY HE DID.

OH.

I'M SORRY.

I WAS SO MAD AT SANDRA, LIKE. I... I DIDN'T WANT TO LET HER GET OFF WITH IT...

JUST RIGHT, TOO.

eh?

YOU SHOULDN'T EVER TAKE SHIT OFF ANYONE, GEMMA. I NEVER DID. BUT YOU DON'T NEED MAGIC OR WHAT-EVER. GET ANGRY IF YOU WANT. CHIN THE WEE BITCH...

CL

IS THAT WHAT YOU DID?

IT IS.

OPEN

AND LOOK WHO I ENDED UP WITH.

JUST MAKE SURE THAT PEOPLE KNOW WHO YOU ARE AND WHAT YOU'RE ABOUT, AND THAT THEY'D BETTER NOT TRY ANY OUL' CUTENESS.

IT'S SOMETHING IN ME I'VE ALWAYS KNOWN ABOUT, BUT NEVER HAD THE BALLS TO FACE...

A VICIOUS, TWISTED LITTLE SHIT OF A THING THAT SCRABBLES IN THE DARK AND GIGGLES TO ITSELF--IT CAN KILL A CHILD IN THE WOMB OR HURT A LITTLE GIRL JUST 'COS SHE'S THE WRONG GUY'S NIECE --

SO I'VE COME HERE TO FIND AN EXPERT ON THE SUBJECT.

CHRIST...!

SHOULD'VE BROUGHT CHAS FOR THIS.

YOU CAN STOP DIGGING NOW, YOU LITTLE BASTARD.

CONSTANTINE

I CALL IT FATE.

I'M FREE.

YOU ALMOST CUT ME IN TWO WITH THAT CURSED SPADE, YOU FOOL!

I SEE THE FAMILY CHARM IS AS STRONG IN YOU AS EVER.

IT'S BEEN TWENTY YEARS, HAS IT NOT? DID YOUR LIFE TURN OUT TO BE THE MAGICAL TRIUMPH YOU EXPECTED?

TOUGH SHIT.

IT HAPPENS TO US ALL. WE GET A SNIFF OF SORCERY AND OH! WHAT PLANS WE MAKE! WE'LL SHAKE CREATION AND LEAVE NOTHING BUT SMILES AND WIT AND A REPUTATION ALL MEN ENVY!

US CONSTANTINES.

I KNEW I WASN'T THE FIRST CONSTANTINE TO DO WEIRD SHIT--A QUICK DEKKO AT THE HISTORY BOOKS TOLD ME THAT...

BUT OLD BRENDAN, ALWAYS THE SCHOLAR, FOUND ME AN ANCESTOR WHO WAS *STILL ALIVE.*

HARRY CONSTANTINE SERVED WITH *CROMWELL* IN IRELAND, AT THE *DROGHEDA* MASSACRE-- BUT WHERE GOD'S FRIGGING ENGLISHMAN DID IT OUT OF GOOD CHRISTIAN MADNESS, HARRY DID IT FOR THE *LOOT.*

AND THEN HE MET HIS MATCH IN THE RIBBON QUEEN, AND SHE CURSED THE BASTARD TO LIVE FOREVER.

THE SPELL WASN'T *THAT* STRONG, JUST BLOODY AMATEUR STUFF. IF *SOMEONE* WANTED TO, THEY COULD STILL DO HIM IN...

SO THE QUEEN PUT HIM SOMEWHERE NO ONE COULD GET TO HIM.

NO ONE DID.

NOT FOR THREE HUNDRED YEARS.

AND THEN ONE DAY, ALONG COME THIS ARROGANT LITTLE SOD AS INQ ABOUT HIS HERITAGE...HE KNOWS WHAT A SHIT HARRY IS AND ONCE HE'S GOT HIS ANSWERS HE JUST FILLS IN THE GRAVE AGAIN.

'COS HE THINKS HE'S GONNA BE DIFFERENT.

CONSTANTINE

BUT HE'S NOT.

HE'S JOHN CONSTANTINE.

WELL? MORE GUIDANCE AND HISTORY, IS THAT WHAT YOU WANT FROM ME?

A BLOODY FINE NERVE YOU HAVE, AFTER THE LAST TIME!

LET'S GET OUT OF THIS SODDING HOLE, EH?

WHAT RIGHT HAD YOU TO SIT IN JUDGMENT OVER ME? OR HAVE YOU ENDED UP WITH BLOODLESS HANDS?

YOU'D BE THE FRIGGING FIRST!

NO. I HAVEN'T.

I STILL DON'T KNOW WHAT KIND OF FATE IT IS THAT MAKES US INTO BASTARDS. I CAME CLOSE ONCE, BUT...

...I KNOW IT TRIES TO GET US ALL.

US CONSTANTINES.

BUT SOMETHING ELSE WE DO, WE ALL TRY TO *BUCK* FATE. RIGHT DOWN TO THE LAST DROP OF BLOOD, WE STRUGGLE ALL THE WAY.

STUBBORN FRIGGERS.

MAYBE IT'S ALL WE'VE GOT.

MAYBE IT IS.

...ALL COME TO A POINT OF CHOICE. I THINK YOUR NIECE HAS REACHED HERS, AND IF SHE HASN'T ALREADY TURNED FROM THE PATH OF THE DAMNED--A FEW GOOD WORDS FROM YOU SHOULD DO THE TRICK...

THINK THAT'S ALREADY SORTED, MATE...

MM. BUT NOW THE WIND IS FRESHENING, AND THE STARS ARE SLIPPING BACK BETWEEN THE CLOUDS. WE'VE LET A MOMENT'S WARMTH PUT OFF DECISION'S CHILL.

I DON'T WANT TO GO BACK BELOW, JOHN, BASTARD THOUGH I AM.

I WANT TO REST.

YOU'RE A BASTARD ALL RIGHT, HARRY...

BUT ONE BASTARD CAN FORGIVE ANOTHER.

WHO ELSE WILL?

AND THERE'S JUST A TINY MURDER IN THE NIGHT.

I THOUGHT I'D BE ADMITTING MY LIFE WAS A FAILURE, WANTING TO END THE LINE...

NO.

I BUCKED FATE. I BEAT IT.

IT'S NO FAILURE TO BE THE LAST CONSTANTINE...

'COS NOW NO ONE ELSE HAS TO BE.

The End

FORTY

GARTH ENNIS • *writer*
STEVE DILLON • *artist*
TOM ZIUKO • *colors*
gaspar • *letters*
STUART MOORE • *editor*

I HARDLY NOTICE WINTER TURNING INTO SPRING.

I'M DRIFTING THROUGH THE DAYS AND DOING NOTHING, IGNORING THE MAGICIAN'S NEED TO SCRABBLE IN THE DARK...

IT'S NOT THAT I'M CONTENT. BASTARDS RULE AND WANKERS WHINE AND BERKS BEND OVER, CHEEKS SPREAD WIDE...

SOD IT, I DUNNO.

SO THE MONTHS SHOOT BY AND RIGHT NOW GOES WITH 'EM, AND ALL I THINK ABOUT IS LOVE AND WAR TO COME...

AND THEN, THIS MORNING, I NOTICE THE DATE.

HERE, KIT? YOU KNOW WHAT DAY IT IS?

KIT?

John

DAILY Mirror
10 MAY 1993

...d to go home at ...hort notice — My ...unt Jane's awfully ...sick. I'll try and get back tomorrow or the next day. Sorry, big lad.
Love Kit xx

37

MY LIFE'S NOTHING TO CELEBRATE.

IS THAT WHY KIT'S IN BELFAST? WHY CHAS IS SNOWED UNDER? 'COS I'M MEANT TO HAVE A FRIGGING CRAP TIME OF IT?

GOT NO OTHER MATES. OH, I KNOW PEOPLE -- BUT THEY TWIG THERE'S SOMETHING NOT QUITE RIGHT AND KEEP THEIR DISTANCE.

THEY KNOW WHAT HAPPENS WHEN YOU GET TOO CLOSE.

WELL, HERE WE GO, GET DRUNK, GET MAUDLIN, SLIDE ON DOWN...

BLOODY HELL.

I'M FORTY, ALL RIGHT.

HEY, JOHNNY! CATCH!

JESUS--!

I HAVEN'T SEEN YOU SINCE LAST CHRISTMAS! AND YOU PUT *THIS* TOGETHER!

SCREW ME, THIS IS FRIGGIN' GREAT! I THOUGHT I WAS IN FOR ONE *MISERABLE* BLOODY NIGHT...

CAN'T BE DOWN ALL YOUR LIFE, JOHNNY.

er... I MEAN, EVEN *I* HAVE TO TAKE A BREAK FROM THE WAR ON CAPITALISM NOW AND THEN...

BLOODY HELL, IT'S NIGEL ENGELS...

NEVER THOUGHT I'D SEE *YOU* ON ME BIRTHDAY, SON.

WELL, YEAH. YOU GAVE ME QUITE A BIT TO THINK ABOUT, WITH THE ROYAL THING...

NOT JUST YOU, NIGE. NOTICE HOW HE HAD SOME PUBLIC TROUBLE WITH THE MISSUS, JUST AFTER WE FINISHED? *POSSESSION* LEAVES YOU WITH *SCARS...* I HEAR HE GOT UP TO SOME WELL DODGY STUFF IN THE BEDROOM. AND... WELL...

I'M NOT GONNA DRAW YOU A PICTURE.

IS HE THE NIGEL ARCHER WANTED TAE DO THE *VOODOO* OAN *THATCHER,* AYE?

THAT'S HIM, HEADER.

BLOODY *IDIOT...*

I MEAN, DIDN'T HE KNOW WHO SHE HAD ON *HER* SIDE?

44

I HAD HOPED WE WOULD IGNORE THE COLD FACADE THAT OUR KIND DEEMS SO NECESSARY, IF ONLY AT THIS TIME OF CELEBRATION.

BUT I SEE THERE WILL BE NO HANDS CLASPED AGAINST THE DARK THIS NIGHT...

I SEE I MUST REMAIN A STRANGER.

OH CHRIST, THE POOR BASTARD...! ALL THOSE YEARS ON HIS OWN AND I...

I....

uh...

HUH-HUH... HHUP!

HAHA HAHA HAHAHA!!

THE OTHERS THINK IT'S PRETTY FUNNY TOO--

SERVES THE POMPOUS SHITE RIGHT! SLEEKIT LOOKIN' *WANKER!*

OH, YOU BRITS... YOUR SENSE OF HUMOR IS SO *ANAL...*

AW, ZATANNA! IMAGINE THE LOOK ON HIS FACE!

WHAT'S THAT?

ROCKET FUEL.

HEY, HEADER? I MEANT TO ASK YOU-- YOU KNOW WHERE TERRY BUTCHER IS THESE DAYS?

AYE, AH'LL TELL YE WHERE HE IS-- HE'S AT THE BOTTOM O' THE CLYDE WI' A *BASEBALL BAT* UP HIS *ERSE!*

AH CAUGHT THE WEE FRIGGER IN BED WI' MA *DAUGHTERS,* FER CHRIST'S SAKE!

MAGGIE AND KATE? AREN'T THEY...?

SIAMESE TWINS, AYE.

THEY LEFT HIM AN INCH TAE PEE WITH, THOUGH...

BUTCHER'S BETTER AFF *DEID,* MIND. HE PISSED AFF *MIKE ADAMS* LAST YEAR AN' GOAT HIS *DICK* CUT OFF...

OLD ADAMS ALWAYS WAS A BIG SOFTY.

48

TWO GRAND AND A JAR OF ANGEL SPUNK, FINAL OFFER.

BASSERDS... BASSERDS... ALL FRIGGIN' BASSERDS...!

EH? CONS'TINE! D'YOU SPIKE M'EFFIN BROC'LI?

WHAT... IS THE MEANING... OF THIS...?

MR. S. THING
THE SWAMP

YOU INVITED *HIM*? BLOODY HELL, MATE!

AW, COME ON. YOU TWO GO BACK *AGES*...

WELL, NOW YOU KNOW HOW I FEEL, TRYING TO TALK TO A BLOKE WHO SPEAKS AT SOD ALL MILES AN HOUR! GROW SOME EXTRA VOCAL CHORDS, YOU BERK!

AND IT'S ME *BIRTHDAY*.

INVITED... TO WHAT? I AM BECOMING... IMPATIENT...

I... DID NOT KNOW. I BEAR YOU NO... ILL WILL... AS SUCH--

OH, LUCKY OLD ME...

SHIT. I'M SORRY, LADS...

ALL RIGHT, ALL RIGHT! DON'T TAKE THE HUMP, SPROUT-BOLLOCKS!

I'VE GOT THIS FRIGGIN' MAGIC IDEA...

HEADER, TAKE NIGE HOME AND PICK UP HIS PLANT, WILL YOU?

WE'LL KEEP A RED FLAG FLYIN' HEEERE...

50

HERE WE GO... SHIT, IT'S BEEN BLEEDIN' AGES...!

I'M DEAD GOOD AT THIS, Y'KNOW. 'S THE CARDBOARD BIT AT THE END'S THE TRICKY BIT... APPARENTLY THEY DON'T DO THAT IN AMERICA...

NO. SO HOW DID YOU MEET JOHN, NIGEL?

WELL... OUR STUDENT UNION WAS HAUNTED, RIGHT? THIS SOCIOLOGY STUDENT JUMPED OUT A WINDOW ON ACID, AN' THEN HE CAME BACK...

SO CONSTANTINE SHOWED UP OUT OF NOWHERE AND SAID HE COULD GET RID OF IT. I THOUGHT HE WAS GOING TO DO AN EXORCISM...

THING WAS, HE SAID IT WAS THE CRAPPEST GHOST HE'D EVER SEEN...

HE JUST WALKED UP TO IT AND SAID "PISS OFF".

AND IT DID.

ALWAYS SEEM TO SCREW IT UP AT THE END.

I KEEP HEARING ABOUT THESE HUGE ONES YOU CAN DO, BUT IT SOUNDS A BIT OF A MYTH IF YOU ASK ME...

SIX IN THE MORNING...

TAKE CARE, YOU LUNATIC. PLEASE.

LISSEN, I LOVE YOU. YOU'RE BEW'FUL...

YOU'RE PLAYING WITH FIRE, LITTLE BOY...

CHEERS, LADS. I'LL BE IN TOUCH.

EXCELLENT, JOHN. HEADER WILL NO DOUBT BE IN A FOUL MOOD WHEN ENGLAND ONCE AGAIN THRASH SCOTLAND IN THE CUP, BUT I ALWAYS LOOK FORWARD TO SEEING YOU...

AH, AWA' AN' THROW SHITE AT YERSELF!

SEE YOU, YOU SNEAKY SOD. WE GONNA SORT THIS FRIGGER SOON?

YOU BE CAREFUL ON THE WAY HOME NOW, NIGE...

YEAH, NO PROBS...! YOU'RE NOD SUDGA BAD BASSERD, Y' KNOW 'AT? NOT SO BAAADD...

OH, YEAH...

ALL COPPERS ARE BASTARDS

THERE COMES A POINT AT ALL THE BEST PARTIES WHERE IT'S JUST TWO BLOKES AND A BOTTLE OF WHISKEY...

SO WHAT DO YOU SEE IN THE WHISKEY, JOHNNY?

I SEE... I SEE... I SEE ONE GODAWFUL FRIGGIN' HANGOVER AND HALF AN HOUR'S AGONY ON THE BOG IN THE MORNING...

IT IS THE MORNING.

mm.

TELL ME, THEN, HOW DOES IT FEEL TO BE FORTY?

I'M OFF TO A BLOODY WEIRD START, ANYWAY...

IT DOESN'T FEEL THAT DIFFERENT. JUST AN EASY WAY TO MARK OFF ANOTHER STAGE, KNOW WHAT I MEAN?

I'VE HAD ONE BUGGERED UP LIFE SO FAR, BUT BLOODY HELL--AT LEAST IT'S BEEN INTERESTING, LIKE.

CHEERS FOR THE PARTY, ANYWAY.

AH, I TOLD YOU I OWED YOU ONE.

IT'S GOOD FOR YOU, ANYWAY. YOU NEED TO LET YOUR GUARD DOWN NOW AND THEN, OR YOU'D FRIG YOURSELF UP ROYALLY.

SO THERE'S THIS PLACE, RIGHT?

AND ALL YOU HAVE TO DO TO GET IN, IS, YOU HAVE TO BE A BLOKE WHO WENT TO CAMBRIDGE...

IN OTHER WORDS, YOUR DAD HAD TO HAVE BEEN RICH ENOUGH TO PUT YOU RIGHT AT THE TOP OF THE SHIT PILE.

THAT WAY, YOU WERE SET FOR LIFE, MATE. YOU WERE UP THERE FOR GOOD, LOOKING DOWN ON ALL THE OTHER ARSEHOLES, AND YOU COULD COME HERE ANY TIME YOU LIKED TO BLOODY WELL REVEL IN IT.

SO THAT'S WHAT THIS PLACE IS: IT'S A CLUB FOR PEOPLE WHO LIKE TO LOOK DOWN ON OTHERS.

SOMETHING HAD BEEN WRONG FOR TWO YEARS NOW.

AND FRIGHTENED AS HE WAS TO ADMIT IT, WHAT WORRIED HIM WAS--

WELL, TO BEGIN AT THE BEGINNING...

HE WAS GABRIEL OF THE CHERUBIM, HE WAS DJIBRIL OF THE EL-KARRUBIYAN,. THOSE BROUGHT NEAR TO ALLAH...

HE SOARED THROUGH THE FIRST SUNRISE AND SANG HIS JOY TO THE FIRST BORN OF THE WORLD, AND EVERY LIVING THING LEARNT HOW TO SMILE.

HE'D WALKED THROUGH BABYLON WITH ROSES IN HIS HAIR. HE'D GIVEN THE SUMERIANS WATER OF LIFE. HE'D COVERED STIRRING SLEEPERS WITH HIS WINGS BE- NEATH THE PYRAMIDS...

IT WAS THE WILL OF THE LORD.

AND...

HE'D BATHED IN ASSYRIAN BLOOD, SPIKED EGYPTIAN INFANTS HIGH ON SPEARS, TORN EYES AND GUTS AND RIBS AND JAWS FROM BODIES OF STILL LIVING MEN--

SODOM AND GOMORRAH DIED IN AN APOCALYPSE OF FIRE, THOUGH WHY ONE MAN SHOULD NOT HAVE ANOTHER, HE DIDN'T KNOW, JUST DID AS HE WAS BID--

THE WILL OF THE LORD.

HE'D COMMITTED RAPE BEHIND A CARPENTER'S IN NAZARETH, AND A CYCLE OF AGONY BEGAN THAT ENDED ON A HILL ABOVE JERUSALEM...

THE WILL OF THE LORD.

IT WAS NOT FOR HIM TO DOUBT. EVERYTHING THAT HAPPENED WAS THE CREATOR'S WILL. NOTHING SURPRISED THE LORD OF HOSTS.

SO...

SO CONSTANTINE WAS RIGHT. THE MAN HE'D SPOKEN TO-- CHARLES PATTERSON--WAS A BULLY AND A RACIST THUG. A SINNER.

SO WHY HAD HE, GABRIEL, EVEN BEEN ALLOWED TO TALK TO HIM? WHY HADN'T HE AT LEAST BEEN REPRIMANDED?

THE WILL OF THE LORD?

AND WHAT WAS WILLED FOR HIM NOW, THEN? WHY WAS HE SUDDENLY HEADED IN THIS STRANGEST OF DIRECTIONS?

HIS HEART FULL OF TROUBLES, THE ARCHANGEL DECIDED TO TAKE THE AIR.

He remembered the look upon the face of Abraham: "Yes, Lord. I will take my son Isaac and make of him a burnt offering to thee..."

Acceptance. Faith. True faith.

How he longed to regain it.

And these sinners walking by, these sheep in their fields... He couldn't even look down on them with that pride he'd treasured in his secret moments...

The doubt had killed it stone dead.

The doubt that Constantine had begun, oh Lord, what was it doing to him?

What?

Oh!

I'm so sorry, I didn't see you! I'm so stupid sometimes...

WELL *DON'T* SAY ANYTHING, THEN! ROTTEN *SNOB!*

THAT--

THAT'S WHAT CONSTANTINE CALLS HIM--AND THAT DEMON WITCH, AND THE WHOLE PACK OF JACKALS--

WAIT!

PLEASE, I-I DID NOT MEAN TO--

I--

I AM SORRY.

WELL, THAT'S... THAT'S OKAY...

I, ah, I SHOULD NOT HAVE BEEN SO HAUGHTY. I WAS DISTRACTED...

I CAN ONLY BEG FORGIVENESS.

OH, YOU DON'T HAVE TO SAY *THAT*... LOOK, ARE YOU ALL RIGHT?

I MEAN, D'YOU WANT TO TALK, OR SOMETHING? BECAUSE YOU SEEM AWFULLY WOUND *UP*...

I... I BELIEVE I WOULD LIKE THAT...

OKAY.

I'M JULIE, BY THE WAY.

GABRIEL.

THAT'S REALLY *NICE*... LIKE THE ANGEL, YOU MEAN? IN THE BIBLE?

YES.

LIKE THE ANGEL.

POCKET SIZED AND EVERYTHING. CHEERS, RICK.

MY PLEASURE.

AH, JOY. NECTAR OF THE GODS...

IF YOU SAY SO. WHAT YOU GOT IN MIND FOR IT, ANYWAY?

NOW JOHN... I HAVE NO MORE INTENTION OF REVEALING MY PLANS FOR THIS THAN YOU HAVE YOURS FOR THAT FINE VOLUME BEFORE YOU...

HMMM?

AH, JOHN. YOU'LL BE IN HEAVEN HALF AN HOUR BEFORE THE DEVIL KNOWS YOU'RE DEAD.

I SHALL BE OFF, THEN...

HEY, JOHN! JOHNNY!

BLOODY HELL! 'EZ! WHERE'VE *YOU* BEEN HIDING?

HIDING *BOLLOCKS*, SON! SEE WHO'S DOWN FROM BRUM?

'LO.

GEORGE...? YOU'VE CHANGED, MATE!

I'LL GET 'EM IN, UH...

REVEREND NEILSEN. *RICK*. A SMALL SHERRY WOULD BE NICE.

S'ME FIRST TIME BACK IN THE SMOKE SINCE '89, JOHN!

'EAST YOU'VE STILL GOT THE ACCENT. FRIG ME... LAST TIME I SAW YOU, YOU WERE WHAT? *EIGHTEEN?*

YEAH. I CAN DO *BRUMMIE*, IF YOU WANT.

" Y'ARRIGHT, LOYKE? BEERMING 'AM, THAT'S ME, LOYKE. ME NAME'S *BAARRY*. SO'S ME MATE'S. AND 'IS. "

NOT BAD. WHY'D YOU LEAVE BRUM, THEN?

IMMENSE GOOD TASTE, I SHOULD IMAGINE...

'COS SOME *BASTARD* BURNT ME HOUSE DOWN, THAT'S WHY.

ME AN' THESE TWO LADS FROM WREXHAM WERE SQUATTIN', RIGHT? SO ONE NIGHT I COME HOME AND THERE'S THIS DICKHEAD ON FIRE IN THE FRIGGIN' GARDEN...

"I COULDN'T BLOODY BELIEVE IT! I WAS TRYIN' TO WORK OUT HOW THE FRIG TO PUT HIM OUT..."

"AN' THEN I SAW WHAT HE'D BEEN UP TO."

DID YOU HELP HIM?

YEAH, WELL...I MEAN, THEY'RE ALL GOING TO HAVE TO WATCH THEIR ARSES IF THEY KEEP TRYIN' THIS SHIT ON US, RIGHT?

YOU SEE THAT THING IN LOS ANGELES LAST YEAR? THAT'S THE CLEAREST BLOODY WARNING THEY'RE GONNA GET, BUT THEY'RE TOO STUPID TO FACE IT...

OI! CONSTANTINE! PHONE FOR YOU!

RIGHT...

YEAH? RIGHT.

TOLD YOU, DIDN'T I?

WE'RE IN BUSINESS, THEN. TAKE IT SLOWLY, RIGHT?

RING US BACK HERE TOMORROW, ABOUT NOON.

GOOD NEWS, JOHN?

YEAH.

FANCY A LITTLE CELEBRATION?

AW, GREAT! JANINE SAYS IT'S DRINKS ON THE HOUSE, LADS!

MY FATHER IS A MAN OF EXTREMES. MORAL DISTINCTIONS ARE, FOR HIM, A SIMPLE QUESTION OF RIGHT AND WRONG.

OF BLACK AND WHITE.

MY BROTHERS AND I ARE THERE- FORE... WE STRIVE TO BE ABOVE REPROACH.

I MYSELF HAVE... ASSISTED IN DISCIPLINING SOME OF THE YOUNGER BOYS.

BUT MY ELDEST BROTHER, THE MOST PROMISING OF US ALL, HE... HE WAS WORSE THAN ANY OF THEM. MY FATHER WAS STERNEST OF ALL WITH HIM.

WHAT HAPPENED TO HIM?

HE FELL.

I CAN HEAR THE OLD DAYS CALLING...

SOME OF THE SHIT I GOT OFF WITH LAST YEAR, IT'S LIKE '83 ALL OVER AGAIN. OUT OF THE SHADOWS AND "ALL RIGHT, SQUIRE? TRUST ME." AND GONE BEFORE YOU KNOW IT.

CHRIST, THAT WAS A LAUGH...

SO I REMIND MYSELF IT WASN'T, IT WAS DEAD MATES AND LOST SOULS AND COLD NIGHTS WITH THE BOTTLE WHILE THE GHOSTS HOWLED ROUND THE DOOR...

AND NOW IT'S DIFFERENT ANYWAY.

KIT...

AND SAYING HER NAME MAKES ME MORE DETERMINED.

AND I ALMOST BELIEVE MY OWN BULLSHIT.

HE TOLD HER MORE TONIGHT THAN HE HIMSELF HAD EVER DARED THINK BEFORE.

"MAYBE YOU WORRY TOO MUCH" SHE SAID. "JUST BECAUSE THIS CONSTANTINE MAKES NASTY REMARKS DOESN'T MEAN YOUR DAD'S ANGRY WITH YOU."

"HE SOUNDS LIKE A RAT, ANYWAY, THIS GUY. FORGET HIM."

EVERY TIME SHE SMILED THERE WAS A LITTLE LAUGH DANCING ON HER LIPS...

YOU LONELY, LUV?

AND SHE'D BE THERE AGAIN TOMORROW, IF HE WANTED TO TALK SOME MORE.

M-MR. PATTERSON?

mmf?

THE BEGINNERS NIETZSCHE

WHAT'RE YOU DOING HERE? I'VE BEEN SITTING HERE ALL NIGHT WAITING FOR YOU TO CALL!

I DIDN'T WANNA PHONE. I'M SCARED, MR. PATTERSON. I'M SHITTING BRICKS!

WHAT D'YOU MEAN? WHAT HAPPENED?

HE ENDED UP TALKING TO SOME DO-GOODER BIRD, THAT'S WHAT!

I MEAN, HE NEAR AS DAMN IT TOLD HER WHO HE WAS!

HE'S SPOOKED, MR. PATTERSON, AND I'LL TELL YOU WHO'S BLOODY WELL DOING IT: CONSTANTINE.

I WANT OUT OF THIS, ALL RIGHT? IT'S GETTING WELL OUT OF ORDER-- D'YOU EVEN REMEMBER WHAT HE IS, FOR GOD'S SAKE?

AND IF THAT CREEPY SOD'S STICKING HIS NOSE IN, THAT'S IT. I QUIT!

NO

YOU

FRIGGING

DON'T

RIGHT.

GET OUT'VE HERE. *NOW.* RIGHT FRIGGIN' NOW...

I MEAN IT...

BE EASIER IF YOU DON'T GIVE US ANY TROUBLE, LUV. YOU'VE GOT THE WRONG BOYFRIEND, THAT'S ALL THERE IS TO IT...

GRAB HOLD'VE HER, WILL YOU, SAM?

YOU'LL BE SORT OF A WARNING, KNOW WHAT I MEAN?

LAST CHANCE, SON.

I THINK I'VE SHAT MESELF! *HAHAHAHA!*

HAHAHAHAHA! YOU HEAR THIS, MICKEY? IT'S ME LAST CHANCE!

GOOD GOD...!

YES...YES... SLOW **DOWN,** WILL YOU?

NO, FORGET HER.

HHHH....

WHAT'S UP?

APPARENTLY THE BITCH HAS TEETH...

I THINK-- WELL, LIKE IT OR NOT, WE'RE GOING TO HAVE TO TAKE CONSTANTINE DIRECTLY.

...ET A CAR READY, AND THE ...PPROPRIATE NEANDERTHALS, ...I'M COMING TOO.

...RIGHT...YOU OKAY, MR. PATTERSON?

FINE.

...WELL, LOOK, CHAS: IF YOU SEE HIM, TELL HIM NOT TO GO HOME. TELL HIM I'M IN THE **GREEN MAN** UP NEAR MUSWELL HILL AND I WANT TO SEE HIM **NOW**, RIGHT?

AYE, I KNOW IT'S A LONG WAY--NO, I'M NOT IN TROUBLE--

CHAS, WOULD YOU JUST **DO** IT FOR US, **PLEASE**?

AW, I'M SORRY. OKAY. AYE.

'BYE.

SHE'D BEEN DOING PRETTY WELL, SHE THOUGHT. KNOCK THE BADDIES' SHITE IN, GET TO SOMEWHERE SAFE, SWITCH ON THE OUL' ICE WOMAN BIT AND GET READY TO GIVE CONSTANTINE THE BALLACKIN' OF HIS LIFE--

AYE, WELL. NOBODY'S PERFECT.

LAD[I]

WAKE HIM UP.

AAAH--!

I THOUGHT IT WAS MEANT TO BE IMPOSSIBLE TO SNEAK UP ON YOU, CONSTANTINE.

LOSING YOUR TOUCH.

YEAH. ME DICKLESS LITTLE SHIT DETECTOR MUST BE ON THE BLINK.

NICE ONE, SCHWARZENEGGER. BEEN GIVING IT A BIT EXTRA ON THE FIVE-KNUCKLE SHUFFLE, HAVE WE?

SHOW HIM HIS FRIEND.

YOU SHOULD'VE STAYED AWAY FROM THE ARCHANGEL, YOU KNOW. NOW...

WELL, WHAT CAN I SAY?

DEZ?

TAKE THE BAG OFF.

NNNNN

HNNNNNN

AW NO! AW BLOODY HELL, NO!!

I THINK THEY WANT TO BE ALONE...

SEE YOU LATER...

DEEEZZ!!

DUNNO. WASN'T HERE AT LUNCH.

WELL, IS THERE SOMEONE WHO WAS? IT'S *IMPORTANT*...

CAROL WAS. LEAVE HER 'TIL SHE'S NOT SO BUSY, RIGHT?

RIGHT, RIGHT...

CAROL! HEY, CAROL, YOU SEEN ME BROTHER?

HELLO, GEORGE!

DEZ, INNIT? HE WAS HERE WITH JOHN WOZZNAME, JUST AFTER LUNCH. WHAT'S WRONG, ANY-WAY?

HE WAS MEANT TO BE HOME AT *TWO*--ME MUM'S WORRIED *SICK*, Y'KNOW?

NOT SURPRISED, IF HE'S OUT WITH JOHN CONSTANTINE.

WHAT... WHAT D'YOU MEAN?

BLOKE'S BAD LUCK, INNE? FRIGGIN' *JONAH*...

MARTIN!

WELL, HE *IS*. WHAT ABOUT THAT RITCHIE SIMPSON, *eh*? CONSTANTINE'S MATE? BURNT TO A CRISP DOWN THE FACTORY...AN' THAT *NUN* HE USED TO HANG ABOUT WITH--THEY FOUND HER HEAD SPIKED AT THE TOP'VE THEM BLOODY STAIRS AT MORNINGTON CRESCENT...

THANK *YOU*, MARTIN.

LOOK, GEORGE, JOHN'S ALL RIGHT, OKAY? AND I'M SURE DEZ IS FINE TOO...

CAROL, IS THAT *BATES* LAD STILL LIVING IN KILBURN?..

OH, HE'S BAD NEWS, GEORGE...

BATESEY? GEORGE FOSTER, REMEMBER?

YEAH, I *KNOW* YOU STILL OWE ME ONE.

YOU STILL LOOKING AFTER THAT SAWN-OFF FOR JOE HOLLIS?

YEAH? EVEN BETTER.

I NEED IT.

ALL DAY THEY TALKED, AND WHEN TWILIGHT CAME THEY WANDERED UNDER SKIES OF DEEPEST, DARKEST BLUE...

THEY LOOKED FOR ALL THE WORLD LIKE LOVERS.

GABRIEL KNEW IT, TOO. THOSE EYES THAT SPARKLED FULL OF GOODNESS, THE LIPS THAT SPREAD INTO DELIGHTED SMILES...

THE LIFE AND JOY AND TRUTH AND PURITY...

OH FATHER, REJOICE.

WHATEVER IT WAS YOU WANTED THEM TO BE... THIS GIRL IS IT.

ARE THESE CHERRY TREES?

I BELIEVE SO, JULIE. THEY ARE.

I LOVE THEM IN THE SPRING, DON'T YOU? WITH THE BLOSSOM?

I THINK I'M HAPPIEST IN SPRING.

WHAT COULD IT HURT?

104

NO GUILT,
GABRIEL.

THE WEIGHT
SLIPPED
FROM HIS
SHOULDERS,
AT LONG
LAST...

NO
GUILT.

KIT.

NEXT:
GOD HELP
THE GUILTY

DEZ DIED AN HOUR AGO.

HE COULDN'T BREATHE WITH HIS THROAT CRUSHED, AND ALL I HEARD WAS A SOFT LITTLE HISS OF A RATTLE, SLIDING OUT FROM THE BUTCHER'S SHOP THAT USED TO BE HIS MOUTH.

SORRY, OLD SON. I'LL SEE YOU SOON.

AND KIT... SOMETHING'S HAPPENED TO HER, AND I CAN'T DO A THING.

I'VE LET HER DOWN.

I ALWAYS KNEW I WOULD.

FEAR and LOATHING | PART THREE
DOWN TO EARTH

GARTH ENNIS • *writer*   **STEVE DILLON** • *artist*
TOM ZIUKO • *colors*   *gaspar* • *letters*
STUART MOORE • *editor*

COME ON IN. I DON'T BITE, YOU KNOW!

I-I AM FINE...

WELL, IT'S NOT MUCH, BUT IT'S HOME...

GABRIEL... D'YOU MIND IF I ASK YOU...?

IS THIS YOUR FIRST TIME?

OH NO!

I MEAN, NOT LIKE THIS, OR, OR--

YES.

IT'S OKAY.

WHY WAS THE COON CARRYING ALL THE LITERATURE? SEVERAL COPIES OF THE NEWSPAPER, OUR POSTERS... KNOW YOUR ENEMY, IS THAT IT?

OR ARE YOU UP TO SOMETHING?

DOESN'T MATTER.

YOU THINK I'M A STUPID MAN, DON'T YOU?

I MEAN, OBVIOUSLY I'M NOT. I HIT YOU AS SOON AS YOU WENT NEAR THE ANGEL, BUT...

IT'S NICE TO HAVE SOMEONE TO LOOK DOWN ON, ISN'T IT?

BUT ALL THE SAME, YOU PROBABLY THINK: "PATTERSON? THAT LITTLE SHIT? I COULD HAVE HIM FOR BREAKFAST. HE'S JUST SOME TOSSER GOT CHUCKED OUT OF PUBLIC SCHOOL, NO BETTER THAN THE ARSE-HOLES HE'S IN CHARGE OF..."

BECAUSE WE'RE ALL SCARED, CONSTANTINE. WE'RE SCARED OF LOSING THE LITTLE WORLDS WE'VE HACKED OUT FOR OURSELVES, AND IF WE SEE SOMEONE TRYING TO TAKE THEM AWAY FROM US...

THAT'S *GREAT*. WE DON'T HAVE TO BE SCARED ANYMORE.

WE CAN HATE.

THAT'S WHERE I COME IN, YOU SEE.

"LOOK AT THOSE BLOODY NIGGERS," I SAY. "LOOK AT THEM COMING OVER HERE LIKE THEY OWN THE PLACE, TAKING OUR JOBS, SCREWING OUR WOMEN... FRIGGING *PAKIS* TAKING OUR BUSINESSES AWAY..."

WORKS A TREAT.

OF COURSE, THE LIBERALS MAKE THEIR FILMS AND SO ON--SEARING INDICTMENTS OF THE STUPIDITY OF RACISM, WITH CLEVER PLOTS AND METAPHORS THAT *DRIP* WITH INSIGHT...AND PEOPLE SAY "YES! IT *IS* WRONG TO HATE A MAN FOR THE COLOR OF HIS SKIN!"

AND THEN THEY GO DOWN THE PUB, AND TWO MINUTES LATER THEY'RE TELLING PAKI JOKES AGAIN.

YOU TALK TOO LOUD IN THE FRIGGIN' *PUB*, ARSEHOLE-- YOU AN' THOSE NAZIS DOWN THE KING'S HEAD! WHERE YOU GOT 'EM?

WH-WHAT? COME *ON*, MATE! *PLEASE!*

"SO WE GOT 'EM, RIGHT? CONSTANTINE AN' 'IS BLOODY *MONKEY!* FRIG THE BOTH'VE 'EM!"

I'VE BEEN UP ALL NIGHT LOOKIN' AN I *WANT* ME *BROTHER!* *WHERE?!*

PUTNEY! OLD FIELD OFF THE TRACKS, IN THIS SHED AT THE BOTTOM! I SWEAR!

RIGHT...

DON'T KILL ME!

RELAX.

YOU NEVER TOLD ME, FATHER

DIDN'T KNOW

COULD NEVER HAVE DREAMED

SHE'S

SHE FEELS LIKE

HEAVEN

FATHER

OH MY FATHER

WHAT SHE DOES

WITH HER FINGERS--

GABRIEL?

119

ALL RIGHT, CHARLIE-- WHY DON'T YOU STICK YOUR SPEECHES BACK UP YOUR ARSE AND TELL ME WHAT YOU WANT WITH THE SNOB?

h? HOLD ON A MINUTE, BOYS.

I'M SURPRISED YOU HAVE TO ASK...

YOU *KNOW* THIS COUNTRY'S GOING TO TURN NASTY IN A FEW YEARS, CONSTANTINE. YOU CAN SEE THE WAY IT'S HEADING...

I MAY NOT BE AN EXPERT ON *MAGIC*, BUT I KNOW IT HELPS TO HAVE SOME MYSTIC CLOUT IN AFFAIRS OF STATE.

AND YOU CAN'T CLOUT MUCH HARDER THAN A FALLEN ARCHANGEL, CAN YOU?

WELL...

CHARLIE, YOU HAVEN'T A *HOPE* OF CORRUPTING HIM. HOW WERE YOU GONNA DO IT? GET HIM TO SAY THE LORD'S PRAYER BACK-WARDS?

YOU'RE TOO LATE, ANYWAY. I'VE DONE IT. HE FELL *TONIGHT*.

SO YOU UNTIE ME, AND FETCH ME SILK CUT...

AND I'LL GIVE HIM TO YOU ON A PLATE.

MUST BE GETTING SOFT. ANYONE ELSE GAVE ME A BOLLOCKING LIKE KIT DID THIS MORNING, I'D'VE JUST PISSED OFF ON 'EM...

HAVE TO SMOOTH HER OVER LATER.

BIT OF CROWING TO DO NOW.

ELLIE?

THAT'S ME.

ANY TROUBLE?

EASY-PEASY. SMELT HIM A MILE OFF.

SHOP AT SPAR

DID HE DO THE CHERRY BLOSSOM?

YEAH, YOU WERE RIGHT. THE BIG SOPPY GIT...

FIVER YOU OWE ME.

I'M IN TROUBLE WITH YOUR OPPOSITION, REMEMBER? YOU WOULDN'T HELP ME BEFORE. HAD TO FIX IT ME OWN WAY. PISSED 'EM OFF.

AS FOR ME, I JUST WANTED TO SEE YOU SCREWED.

WHY?

YOU'RE ME NEW MINDER.

I AM NOTHING OF YOURS, CONSTANTINE. THAT SHRED OF PRIDE—IT'S ALL I HAVE LEFT, NOW.

THIS IS THE ONLY THING KEEPING YOUR ARSE OUT OF THE FIRE.

CHRIST, I HATE BEING THE BEARER OF BAD NEWS.

BEEN DOING ME HOMEWORK, GABE. ACCORDING TO A LITTLE BOOK I BOUGHT RECENTLY...

SHOP AT SPAR

AT THE END OF IT, HE ASKED CONSTANTINE HOW HE'D BE SURE HIS HEART WAS SAFE. AND CONSTANTINE TURNED TO HIM, AND SMILED A SMILE HE'D BE SEEING IN HIS NIGHTMARES...

"TRUST ME."

NO MORE SNOB, THEN. NO MORE PRIDE.

JUST A FRIGHTENED, FALLEN ANGEL...

LYING IN THE DIRT.

THE END

GARTH ENNIS • *writer*   **STEVE DILLON** • *artist*   **TOM ZIUKO** • *colors*
TODD KLEIN • *letters*   **JULIE ROTTENBERG** • *assistant editor*   **STUART MOORE** • *editor*

SHE WAS NERVOUS.

SHE COULD'VE WRITTEN HIM A LETTER, BUT THAT WAS A STUPID WEE GIRL'S THING TO DO, AND SHE HATED CHICKENING OUT OF ANYTHING....

GOD, THOUGH, THIS WAS GONNA DESTROY HIM. SHE'D SEEN ENOUGH OF THE REAL HIM TO KNOW THAT.

TYPICAL ...!

AYE, RIGHT ENOUGH. MEN WOULD TAKE YOU FOR GRANTED, COME TO RELY ON YOU--YOU'D BE LIKE A FRIGGIN' FOUNDATION HOLDIN' THEM UP, HALF THE TIME--

BIG BLOODY KIDS.

BUT ALL THE SAME...

ALL RIGHT?

HIYA.

YOU'RE TALKING TO ME AGAIN, THEN. 'BOUT BLOODY TIME...

I'M AWAY BACK TO BELFAST, JOHN.

FOR... FOR HOW LONG?

FOR GOOD.

I'M FED UP WITH THIS TOWN. IT SMELLS ROTTEN, SO IT DOES. AND THE PEOPLE CARRY ON LIKE -- I DUNNO. IT'S LIKE THEY'RE BEATEN. THEY'VE NOTHING LEFT IN THEM.

I WANT TO GO HOME AND SEE ALL MY FRIENDS AGAIN, NOT JUST TALK TO THEM ON THE PHONE...

AND I DON'T WANT TO BE WITH YOU ANYMORE, JOHN.

LOOK... I MEAN...

KIT... I KNOW THAT WAS ROUGH, THOSE TWO ARSEHOLES LAST WEEK--

YOU PROMISED NOT TO DO THAT STUFF ROUND ME, REMEMBER?

I DON'T WANT YOU TO BE PERFECT. I JUST WANT A QUIET LIFE WITHOUT SOME BASTARD KICKING MY DOOR DOWN AND COMING AT ME WITH A *SWITCHBLADE*.

YOU LET ME DOWN.

BUT I DIDN'T EVEN KNOW ABOUT THEM!

YEAH, BUT YOU KNOW WHAT I GET UP TO! YOU CAN'T EXPECT TO BE LEFT OUT OF IT FOREVER!

NOBODY'S *PERFECT*, LUV...

A QUIET LIFE? SO YOU'RE MOVING TO BELFAST?

OH, DON'T BE SO BLOODY STUPID!

YOU'VE NEVER EVEN BEEN THERE, YOU DON'T KNOW WHAT YOU'RE TALKIN' ABOUT.

KIT, THIS IS--PLEASE, LUV, I THOUGHT WE--

I'VE NEVER GOT THIS CLOSE TO ANYONE BEFORE, RIGHT? *NEVER.* I'VE NEVER FELT SO *GOOD,* EITHER. AND I DEFINITELY NEVER SAID STUFF LIKE THIS TO ANYONE IN MY *LIFE.*

I....

AND NOW YOU'VE RUINED IT ALL, JOHN.

BLOODY HELL....

HOW DID YOU GET TO BE SO *COLD?*

WELL?

COME ON, JOHN! WHAT WAS THAT ALL ABOUT?

LEAVE OFF, WILL YOU, CHAS?

NO, I BLOODY WON'T! YOU WERE BEIN' A RIGHT ARSEHOLE -- LIKE ONE OF THESE MAD OLD BASTARDS WHO RABBITS ON ABOUT NOT FIGHTING THE WAR FOR LAYABOUTS LIKE US, ALL THAT SHIT!

AND HAVE YOU SEEN THE FRIGGIN' STATE'VE MY FACE?

KIT LEFT ME.

OH SHIT.

THAT'S NOT SO BAD, IF SHE LET YOU STAY 'TIL FRIDAY.

RA-RA.

WELL, I'M SORRY ANYWAY.

MM.

RIGHT, I'LL SHUT ME MOUTH. I KNOW HOW YOU FEEL, LIKE...

CHAS, YOU DON'T HAVE A FRIGGIN' CLUE HOW I FEEL. WHAT WOULD YOU KNOW, LIVING WITH THAT FAT BITCH?

SO JUST SHUT UP, FOR GOD'S SAKE...

NOW JUST A BLOODY MINUTE--!

OH, BOLLOCKS...

PISS OFF, WILL YOU, CHAS? GO BACK WHERE YOU BELONG, WITH ALL THE OTHER ARSEHOLES.

THINK... IT'S... MIDNIGHT...

BEEN MARKING OFF THE HOURS WITH WHISKEY.

WHAT'D BRENDAN CALL IT?

BOTTLED SUNSHINE, THAT'S WHAT HE SAID.

DOESN'T LOOK LIKE SUNSHINE TO ME. SLOPS IN THE BOTTLE LIKE A WINO'S PISS, DARK AND SOUR AND ROTTEN...

FRIGGIN' SHIT!!

AH, JESUS...

JESUS...

GOOD JOB I'VE GOT ANOTHER ONE

DARK AND DEADLY!

CONTEMPORARY GRAPHIC NOVELS FROM TITAN BOOKS!